LIVE LIKE *crazy*

My will to heal in the wake of breast cancer

Sally Ann Nisberg

Life...
Embrace it –
Own it –
Live Like Crazy.
Hugs,

Published by:
Sally Ann Nisberg
227 Miraflores Dr.
Palm Beach, FL 33480
snisberg@gmail.com

Editor: Randy Wood
Cover design: Sally Nisberg, Brooke Erin Debany, and MetroInk
Interior design: Randy Wood
Cover photo: Brooke Erin Debany
All photos courtesy of Sally Nisberg unless otherwise noted.

ISBN: 978-0-9964080-0-4
Library of Congress Control Number: 2015945851

Printed in the United States of America

Strength, not fear

Hope, not despair

Joy, not sadness

Optimism, not frustration

Success, not defeat

Contents

Acknowledgements

Breast cancer and its invasion of our lives is a family affair.

No doubt, a breast cancer diagnosis shatters our routine and day-to-day lives; managing the intrusion is a trying task.

Suddenly and without warning, a lump in my breast threw us head first into the world of cancer. My husband jumped right into the trenches with me, adapted to changes, often daily, that offered no road map or rule book.

The cancer fight, the challenge, the havoc you go through, well, it's hard on our spouses, too. It's cruel and emasculating. It's essentially the helplessness that complicates and messes with our partners, the ones who promise to take care of us.

My husband's fears and concerns about this disease, its treatment, debilitating and unpredictable symptoms, recurrence and uncertainty, his shock, disbelief and helplessness were never revealed to me.

Like everything else my husband has conquered in life, the fright, devastation and grief were initially shocking, yet, he never allowed himself to appear unprepared for each stage of my recovery.

It is my husband who urged me to share my story, to write this book and to help others.

Breast cancer violated my body and "our" life. I have experienced every emotion on the planet in navigating my way through many dark moments and my husband, who always chooses to act with strength and love, was and will always be my light. My love.

Thank you, Babe, for all you are. Again and again you prove that everything is manageable and our life is a gift to be treasured. XXOO

৪০ ୯୫

Beauty, Grace and Grit.

Where to begin in thanking you for being there with and for me through the terror of breast cancer, is certainly not the case, Jackie. Your calls, assurances and support during surgeries and treatments were life saving. Whatever the schedule, you were on a flight and at my side.

Your love and dedication to family is extraordinary, and I am grateful for a very special sister who insisted I fight, heal and thrive.

Love you dearly....

Life ~ Embrace it ~ Own it ... Live Like Crazy

My children: Love you to the moon and back!

෨ ෬

Grateful for your love.

I am humbled and often reminded of the sea of love and support from my family and friends.

Every one of you who reached out, who embraced and cared for me, has left a footprint on my heart.

You calmed my fears, healed my wounds and fueled my recovery.

We all need to be there with and for each other. Every word, every conversation, every visit matters.

Paying it forward is now my privilege. I love you all and will always have your backs.

෨ ෬

My hope is that some experience, message, page, paragraph, or word in this book inspires you—the patient, survivor or caregiver—to embrace this very moment, meet the challenge, choose not to suffer.

ॐ ॐ

My medical team: I thank you for your dedication and determination to help me beat this monster. What heroes you are to me and all the patients you treat with such caring professionalism.

Live like crazy!

Preface

Why me? Why did I get it? Is it genetic? Is it environmental? Is it just bad luck? Everyone who has been diagnosed with cancer asks these same questions. Cancer does not discriminate based on age, gender, income, race or creed. The news media tells us stories about families where every woman for three or four generations has died from or been treated for breast cancer, which suggests a strong genetic link. A 2015 study by two John's Hopkins researchers concluded, "Bad luck explains a far greater number of cancers than do hereditary and environmental factors."

Generally speaking, who gets cancer is pretty random. While we can take steps to minimize our risk factors, such as maintaining good nutrition and exercise, managing stress, getting regular checkups, practicing early detection steps, if you don't smoke and are not exposed to known cancer-causing substances (e.g., asbestos, DDT, Agent Orange, etc.), your risk level of getting cancer is reduced but not eliminated. The Johns

Hopkins study concluded that only about 33% of cancer cases are attributable to environmental causes, the other 66% random cell mutation—the "bad luck" factor.

Cancer isn't one disease; it is more than a hundred diseases that attack various parts of the body. It is once-healthy cells that turn against you, and left to themselves, they'll overtake and kill other healthy cells. If the process isn't stopped, the disease consumes you from within.

I'm making my stand here to fight cancer. I'll use my strength, knowledge and voice to help those with the disease to live through it. I believe that to survive cancer, regardless of prognosis, all cancer patients must *stand for life*. We cancer patients must not let this disease overtake us. We must each choose to live our lives with purpose, living in hope, not fear. We must physically, emotionally and spiritually attack the disease with just as much gusto as our doctors do medically. If we hope to survive, we must attack with a certainty that we will live, live today and live tomorrow. The danger lies in giving up hope and giving into fear. Shutting down physically, emotionally and spiritually and giving into the disease, diminishes the chances for survival.

Despite my message preaching for hope, determination and resilience, I must recognize here that many brave souls do lose their fight against cancer. If you are concerned that I am saying your sister or mother did not survive because she did not fight hard enough, please don't misunderstand me. Sadly, for too many people, the diagnosis comes too late, after the disease has progressed too far, too rapidly to make long-term survival an option. I'm certain they carried themselves with courage, and many of them did wondrous things with their lives post diagnosis. My message is, whether the prognosis is good or not, I want all patients to fight on; to live life to its fullest, with as much passion and energy as you can. Embrace your family and loved ones. Do the things you most enjoy. See the places you want to see. Live each day you have left as fully as you can—Live Like Crazy!

As I write this book, I have to remind myself that I am talking to a large group of people who may have or has had cancer, or who cares for someone who does. There are a million new patients each year in the US. Medicine has advanced rapidly in the past 20 years, making the prognosis for many cancer patients very positive. I understand however that is not the case for all patients. For all the positive messages posted on various social media sights, we still hear of too many friends who were taken by this awful disease. My remarks in this book and the advice I offer here are hopeful to a fault because I believe this disease can and must be beaten.

Victim? Patient? Survivor?

Who am I now? Am I a cancer victim? A patient? A survivor? Can I just be me? Does cancer steal my identity, too? Why not just be me, Sally?

People during their cancer journey identify themselves or are identified with one of these labels—victim, patient, survivor. I think that is natural in a way. It goes along with the stages of grief we go through when we are told we have cancer. We initially feel like a victim, angry about the situation we are facing. Then a patient as our treatments progress and we rationalize what is going on, telling ourselves we can do this, just five more treatments, whatever we need to tell ourselves to get through. And finally we feel relief at being a survivor when the doctors say our tests are clear, accepting that we have come through the storm, happy to be alive.

We hear it a lot in the media as they tell the stories of survivors' walks and runs, fund-raising events for research or services for patients, or when a celebrity who has been diagnosed and speaks out about what's going on in her life and how she hopes to help others with her story. For any woman who has identified herself as a wife, a mother, a sister, it can be uncomfortable taking on a different label.

But the thing with labels is, they are often how other people see you and understand what you are going through. Labels help others understand something about you. The labels may not be comfortable for you and they never capture the whole you. You have permission to just be you, to see yourself as you always have.

I will many times in this book tell you that it is okay to feel how you feel. You will certainly go through a variety of emotions on your journey. Some days you may feel like a victim, especially early on when you've just been diagnosed and your brain is so full of questions and emotions. If the labels feel like they fit you, that is okay, and if they don't, that is okay, too.

There is no correct or preferred label for people on this journey. Well, maybe there is one. It is You. You are and always will be You. You may feel like a victim early on. As you move from diagnosis to treatment, you will feel like a patient as you endure surgery and medical treatment. And when all is said and done, you may feel like a survivor, that you've come through the gauntlet battle scarred and tested but alive. At the core though, it is you. My hope is that the labels never overtake who you are at the core. They are transitional and temporary at best but you remain. I have introduced myself as each of these at some point in my journey. I was a victim for a short time.

I was a patient and now am on my survivor's journey. However, all through it, I was, and am, Sally. I was Sally who had breast cancer.

Each phase of that journey taught me something about myself. I didn't get stuck in one label or another, and I hope you don't either. The lessons I learned along the way are the gifts I want to share with other women who are on this journey or may be someday, however cancer may touch their lives.

Fear

Cancer is a monster. Aside from cancer itself, a patient's biggest enemy is fear. Fear paralyzes us. It affects our thinking, our decisions, our actions, and our well-being. For all my family and friends who know me and helped support me through my diagnosis and treatment, they will tell you I appeared like a rock, strong and determined to get through the treatments, to beat cancer's ass and to come out stronger. I confess, internally I was a mess. I had just enough strength to get through each day. I was constantly afraid that cancer was going to kill me, and I didn't want to die. I was at the end of my chemo treatments when my internist, Dr. Mark, seeing the fear behind my eyes, called me to task. "Sally, you look like hell; relax, you're not going to die." It was a moment of reassurance that I needed. At that point, I let go of the fear and was finally able to focus on getting better. I was healthy again and I would survive. I could breathe again.

I hope to accomplish two things with this book. First, I want to share my story. It was perhaps the most difficult time in my life and I believe I am a better person for it. Second, I want to help others on their cancer journey to learn to make good choices and to take action for themselves. I am a life coach and I work a lot with cancer patients. My family, my friends and many of their friends have called me, emailed me, to tell me they have been diagnosed with cancer. That time in a person's life feels like you are a person adrift at sea. Your boat has sunk and it's just you in the water. You are desperate to find another survivor, someone to cling to, who will give you hope. These family and friends know my story and are reaching out to me for help. They are asking me what's next? What steps do I take? Will I survive this nightmare? Can I kill this monster?

Based on my work and conversations with doctors, caregivers, other patients and survivors, I offer what I feel are the key steps, my coaching points if you like, cancer patients need to take to help move themselves through their cancer journey successfully. Please understand, these steps are not an alternative to proper medical treatment. They are intended to help someone focus on their own wellness post diagnosis and to help them overcome the paralysis and fear with which cancer hits us.

In addition, I hope this book offers caregivers, be they doctors, nurses, technicians, family and loved ones, insights into the hearts and minds of cancer patients. There will be times when your patient needs to lean on you, physically, emotionally, mentally and spiritually. We need your bravery and strength as much as we need our own. However, there will be times we just want to be left alone. I hope you will be able to see our individual journeys as a process to achieve wellness.

We breast cancer survivors at every stage of treatment and beyond deserve guidance and support only in a way that we can manage.

I am privileged by the constant flow of survivors and friends of survivors who reach out to me. And am careful in offering support: an ear to listen, a shoulder to cry on, a hand to hold. My objective is to provide each person with resources and reliable information—only if it is needed and wanted. I hope each person feels that they have the power to choose their course. My purpose is to willingly help patients discover what is best for them, rather than to validate my own cancer battle and personal choices.

Every one of us who courageously faces cancer not only has the ability to live a full life—we have the ability and right to live a life full of meaning. We need to enjoy our hobbies or explore a new one that has always spoken to us, do volunteer work; create a focus that connects us to something outside ourselves, our career that evokes success, etc. Get involved (explore, call a friend, have a conversation) as much as you can. Through these efforts, your thoughts and energy level will change, I promise.

People take many paths to reach what matters to them: meditation, prayer, silent observation, connecting with nature, expressing ourselves creatively, serving others or expressing our values by supporting a cause. Do what feels right and works for you, even if that's simply striving to pause and feel the moment.

Don't ignore what you feel. Sharing our emotions helps us heal. Breast cancer has illuminated the things that matter in my life and I keep a mental registry of what is important and I act on honoring and achieving everything that can be attained, earned and enjoyed. Not in an instant, yet patiently and intently, with a sense of appreciation.

As overpowering as it felt at the time, I understand that breast cancer was a brief intermission in my life story. I did not allow it to change my theme and with time, to my surprise, I welcome making edits—to see what I experienced in new lights, and adding the perspectives of others who journeyed with me.

I take great meaning from my religious and spiritual beliefs. Whether we consider ourselves religious or not, we can find extraordinary value in focusing on what is meaningful in our lives. You, too, can find yourself embracing a greater satisfaction with life, freedom from regret and a precious sense of inner peace. It's my hope that cancer can leave behind this gift for each one it touches, once the treatments are done.

When we have the support of others who care about and understand us, it gives us the strength to make life beyond full.

Don't hesitate. Reach out to your community to ensure you have the help and support that you need to cope with your diagnosis, treatment, survival, with your life. This community of support goes well beyond your medical team and, most importantly, to family, trusted friends and a network of others who understand your feelings, your experience.

This book, my story, is not just about how I survived breast cancer; it is about how I wanted to beat the hell out of it. It is about prevailing over fear, pain, tears and sadness. It's about turning my setback into a comeback through the support of my family, friends and an extraordinary medical team that stared into the face of this monster and said, "Cancer, you lose!"

I now realize that my identity isn't that I'm a cancer survivor; rather, I am a loving, caring, talented and creative individual, and cancer was only part of my journey. In hindsight, my life certainly was not shattered by my breast cancer diagnosis. In fact, I have seen opportunities to improve myself that I might have otherwise missed.

I have found that my cancer journey and the gift of conversation that I now rely on, has ultimately benefited me with a much richer life. And I now believe that sharing our experiences, feelings and observations about the emotional, physical and daily challenges promises to gift each of us with tremendous clarity and relief. It is to this purpose that I offer my story, in hopes that other patients and survivors going through the challenges I faced can be more informed about their own journey.

&) CR

Forward

After a routine mammogram and ultrasound, I was informed I had a mass that needed a biopsy. My world was rocked. I was terrified but knew I needed to stay calm and GET INFORMED! Your mind races with fatalistic thoughts—my children, my husband.... We decided to keep it to ourselves—we had no info, only a myriad of what-ifs. I knew I had to speak with someone who had walked this path and to get insight into what I was about to endure. I decided to reach out to my sister-in-law, Sally Ann.

At first I was very worried that I would be bothering her—she had endured so much—did she really need me bringing up all the painful memories? Sally was a rock. She told me step-by-step what to expect. She encouraged me to be my own advocate and search out a doctor/technician I felt gave me the greatest comfort. The morning of my biopsy, there was Sally—in the chair next to me, calming, explaining, sharing.

It was nearly a week of agony awaiting results, complete torture! Although I was very lucky my diagnosis was not cancer, the fear was nearly paralyzing. If not for Sally's kindness and help, I can't imagine how terrified I would have been, nor would I have known the right questions to ask, and advice to seek.

I've had two biopsies now. The second was much easier knowing what to expect, but the panic and fear of those words, "We see a mass," is something no one wants to hear.

— Beth Malsbury
(Sally's sister-in-law)

৩৩ ৫৪

LIVE LIKE *crazy*

Part One—Sally's Story

Who the hell wants to get cancer? I surely didn't. I was healthy, active and worked hard to live a balanced lifestyle.

My life was chaotic at that time. My son had experienced a terrible accident and was in a coma. I was living at the hospital, physically and emotionally. When I found the lump at the bottom of my right breast it was like an electric shock went through my body. This wasn't right. Despite feeling fear, I couldn't focus on what my hands were telling me. I ignored the alarm bells ringing in my head and chose to push my fear down. I told myself I had to be there for my son.

I knew I had a mammogram coming up in a few weeks and I would focus on the lump then. Maybe it was just a cyst and would go away, and the mammogram would show nothing unusual. Honestly, I knew better but call it fear, denial or simply an overpowering mother's instinct; I didn't have time for cancer. I chose to focus on my son.

Surviving breast cancer is an experience that changes us. When we are faced with our mortality, our true self is revealed, and we become grateful for things we previously took for granted. That insight was still ahead of me. At that point in time, I had to manage the whirlwind of diagnosis, consultation, surgery and recovery.

"I'm afraid!"

One-month later I went for my mammogram appointment. It wasn't my first mammogram ever. Over the previous ten years, I'd had several ultrasounds and biopsies, primarily on my left breast due to my having dense breasts and earlier finding two benign lumps there. It's never an easy day, but this exam was more intense. In the waiting room, I filled out the insurance paperwork but not the health screening form, figuring I would just talk with the technician; I am a people person first! I swallowed hard, held my breath and began the process. I don't know if I expected the technician to see the lump with a gasp or a shocked reaction. I didn't fill out the health screening form, I discussed it with the tech so she knew what I had felt. She heard me and confirmed what I felt but since I had not written it down on my survey, it didn't get passed along to the radiologist, which I only learned later. Without my health form indicating I had found a problem, no red flags were raised. I knew the lump was still there but I decided I would wait to see what the scan results showed. Just maybe I was wrong.

Not long after, I received the lab results in the mail. Usually that's a good sign. Doctors' offices call you when it's bad news. Good news comes as a form letter in the mail. I was expecting a phone call from my doctor's office but it never came. I was a little nervous as I opened the letter from my radiologist. I read the words carefully. The letter said they were pleased to inform me that I had checked out fine, and they reminded me to schedule another appointment for next year. I was shaking. This was good news but I wasn't thrilled, as you would think I should have been.

Why? Because I knew the letter was wrong. The mammogram was wrong and I knew it was wrong. I still felt a lump in my right breast; it was inside toward the bottom of my breast. I hadn't gone to see my doctor right away because I was terrified. I didn't have the emotional or mental capacity to deal with the situation. Now I couldn't dodge the truth facing me in the mirror any longer. I had to act.

After I got the follow-up letter from my scan, I called my general physician immediately. I told

29

him I had received the letter from the radiology center saying that I was clear. I explained what I felt, that I knew the scan results were wrong, and that I needed to come in right away. I made an appointment for the next day with my radiologist. Dr. Goodwin examined me and confirmed the presence of the lump. He suggested we do a biopsy. The majority of lumps found in the breast are noncancerous fibroids or cysts that resolve themselves, which had been my experience for a decade. My gut instinct was this was not one of those. Dr. Goodwin explained that without my patient information form stating that I had a concern about a lump, the initial mammogram raised no red flags for them. I later learned that my tumor, diagnosed as a poorly differentiated, Stage 2, ductile carcinoma, is difficult to identify through mammography. Thankfully I knew my body well enough to realize something was wrong and I took action. I agreed to have the biopsy and scheduled it for the next day.

What followed was the most intense ten days of my life. It was like someone hit all the fire alarms and panic buttons at once. My mind exploded with all the what-ifs, how-can-Is and why-mes, and with the overload of information I needed to process. And at the same time, everything seemed to stop, like a slow-motion effect in a movie where everything else around the main character is frozen in time yet they are still aware and moving. I am a wife, a mother, and a professional. I was accustomed to a fast pace and others depending on me. Now it all flipped. I had to look to others to guide, reassure and care for me; which is not the position I am normally used to being in. Normal was not on my radar.

In March 2011, I had a mastectomy to remove my right breast. Fortunately, the margins around the tumor were clean and the prognosis was good. Breast cancer is shocking. It's dreadful when it happens to someone you love, and even worse when it hits even closer to home, when you are the chosen one. It's the most common cancer among American women; about one woman in eight (12%) in the United States will develop invasive breast cancer during their lifetimes, according to the American Cancer Society. Terrifying statistics, yet I chose to completely ignore and even refused to give further thought or consideration to those numbers. What did they have to do with me? They were not important to my treatment and my healing process and only served to frighten and cause me to question my resolve to survive.

No doubt, the fear was still there. It was not immediate, yet I drifted into a period of depression that continued for a year after my first mastectomy. I felt pretty much lost in my effort to step back into life beyond breast cancer. Many months after the completion of my surgeries, first a mastectomy on the right, then my left breast eight-months later, with chemotherapy treatment and reconstruction in between. The fog was so thick and my mood so low, I wasn't able to feel much of anything around me. The conflict in feeling that I had so much to return to and to live for, while also feeling an unshakeable fear of not being convinced I would be healthy, was paralyzing. Research indicates that many survivors may experience depression after cancer, and I have to believe that it strikes us all to some degree. But I knew I could only move forward if I had no doubts about what to do next.

On a calm and lovely Sunday morning a friend shared his metaphoric view of Blue Skies and the choice we make to be our authentic selves. At that very moment as he was speaking, soft white clouds floated across the sky outside the window as if on cue, to be the literal backdrop to his message. His lesson for me was that our lives are like a beautiful blue sky, and the clouds drifting through are simply our challenges floating about dimming our light. Anger, fear and impatience are unleashed emotions that can blind our ability to see two-feet ahead. We all have choices all the time. We can choose to push the clouds away and to soar above in the blue skies.

Funny I knew this. Yet hearing and gaining the view from someone three-years beyond treatment illuminated the simplicity of my choice. Would I dwell in the anger and fear and be blind to the beauty of life around me or soar past them?

Breast cancer treatment and our survival require every ounce of our energy. After treatment our mood plummets. Our experience has been tough, physically and emotionally, and it takes time to recover; we've been exhausted.

Treatment

As I feared, my biopsy results came back positive for cancer. I saw my breast surgeon who called it a poorly differentiated, rapidly advancing, ductal carcinoma, identifying it as Stage 2. Then I met with my oncologist, who performed blood work. She identified it as triple negative. Now, with a clearer diagnosis, we set a treatment plan: surgery then chemotherapy. My doctor was concerned about the speed with which my tumor had grown. It didn't mean that much to me at the time, but I would come to learn that I had good reason to be afraid. Triple negative is a very aggressive form of cancer and only occurs in about 15% of all breast cancer patients. As a fairly uncommon type of cancer, the therapy plan is not as clearly prescribed as it is with other types. As a triple-negative patient, radiation was not an option, so it was a radical mastectomy followed by chemo.

Surgery, for some people the word brings up deep feelings of fear. They think, "Can I just let myself go under the complete control of this person I've just met? What will they find? Is my body full of cancer?" For some people, it's a relief, "At least they'll get the stuff out and I can move on!"

I underwent a mastectomy on the right side. I originally wanted to have both breasts removed, a double mastectomy. My surgeon had asked me to reconsider, to just remove one versus both. In spite of my wishes, I agreed. I did not speak up. I woke up in recovery thinking, "Why didn't I do both?" My surgeon felt he was able to remove the entire mass and my pathology did not reveal extra tissue involvement, the margins were clean. During the same surgery, I underwent what was to be the first of six reconstructive procedures. Post-surgery, I was prepared to begin chemotherapy and healing. I believed this was the best course of treatment for me and that I would be back to my old self in no time. Or so I thought. I spent eight hours in recovery. My blood pressure was very low and took a long time to come back to a normal level.

After surgery, I had about a month to recover and to prepare for chemo. Yet all I could focus on was that I should have had both breasts removed to fight the cancer. I couldn't shake the feeling and I called my surgeon in a panic. I went back to see my surgeon and, though he felt there was time to wait, that it was more important to begin chemo, he would do the surgery if I insisted. My anxiety to get the cancer out of my body was apparent. We scheduled the second mastectomy. The day of surgery, after pre-screening was completed, my surgeon advised me not to do the procedure. He believed that I needed to proceed with the chemo as my first priority rather than perform the second mastectomy, which could delay my chemo treatment. He felt this was a risk we should not take. I listened but I didn't follow my gut. I agreed to follow the new plan he prescribed and we left the hospital.

This was chaos. My emotions were controlling my decision making. My family was in survival mode, trying to support me. The surgical team was taking their lead from me and the surgeon. I was creating chaos because I didn't use my voice to ask for what I needed.

Meanwhile, I saw friends who had gone through treatment and survived breast cancer. I saw the results of their reconstructive surgeries and I questioned mine. As chemo loomed, I didn't give voice to my concerns. My anxiety increased because I didn't ask the questions I should have asked. I followed the plan.

Chemo

How would I feel? Would I get sick? How bad would it be? In everyone's mind, nausea and hair loss are always associated with chemotherapy. How would the space feel while I was in treatment? Could I relax, feel safe, acknowledged?

I think chemo is a grossly misunderstood event in a cancer patient's life. Media gives us such a grey, clinical view of it; it's all cold, fear, loathing and vomiting. In reality, it's not that way today. Chemo treatment has transformed to a patient-focused system. It's caregiving at many levels, from check-in to administering meds. The people in today's treatment centers are caring, compassionate and helpful, oh, and the centers are inviting and embracing, to help patients feel comfortable. I won't call it a day at the spa but all the caregivers and volunteers realize that the entire process is about saving lives. The medical profession knows it's treating sick people who need a kind and helping hand. It's hard but at least it's a caring environment that puts patients first. But that's what I learned as I went through treatment. Before then I experienced all the anxiety many patients feel.

Chemotherapy treatment is like running a marathon. It requires energy to be expended over time so that you can reach the finish line. When I knew I was facing eight treatments (at least four hours per visit) every three weeks for six months, treatment days felt as though they lasted forever and unleashed chaotic thoughts and fears that I promised myself to control and manage through the course of treatment.

Chemo is a word people don't want to hear and certainly not something they want to go through. Tell someone you're in chemo and they'll likely wince. But, for those of us with cancer, we often don't have a choice. I remember how terrified I was of getting my first treatment.

Chemo is a strange experience. It's one part managing your own expectations, another part constant vigilance about your health. And finally, it's another part just managing the process, and shutting down your life in some ways for a year. Bouncing back from treatments takes energy, all you've got. Be ready for the time you need to heal. I won't deny that while in treatment I wasn't always strong and brave. I admit I was afraid and was worried. Each time I sat in my chemotherapy chair, I feared what was flowing through the needle into my vein and my body; would it kill the mutant cells that were trying to kill me? What else would that toxic cocktail do to me? What side effects would I experience? How sick would I get? I worried if I would live.

I was directed to arrive an hour or so early for treatment, to allow time for blood work and to determine whether I was able to receive treatment. If I was not well, or my white cell count was too low, I could not receive treatment due to the risk of infection. It takes tremendous strength and faith to step into a fusion center and it is above all a test of patience. Accepting and understanding the time it takes to prepare for treatment is necessary and in our best interest—breathe—talk to whomever is with you. I learned to do whatever it took to get through each moment. For some patients it was music, crosswords, reading, or whatever else helped to calm them.

My center was bright and open. There were many chemo chairs in stations equipped with TV, Internet access, and best of all, plenty of warm blankets. Volunteers, which I am today, were front and center in making sure I was comfortable.

Once in my infusion chair, the nurse ordered the chemotherapy cocktail and any pre-medications that I required from the pharmacy. Normally, it took at least 30 minutes for the drugs to arrive. Some of the pre-medications may be steroids, anti-nausea medications, whatever my oncologist ordered.

What I liked best was it felt like I was walking into a community. Warm, friendly people offering me snacks, drinks, conversation; whatever I needed, it was met.

Thank goodness, the anti-nausea meds generally worked and I did not experience nausea through treatment. I was intent, from day one to maintain a healthy diet—no junk food! And I believe this discipline played a huge part of my experiencing no ill symptoms. One thing I did was keep myself hydrated. Water is life, and in the case of chemo, it is quality of life. I'll talk more about this later but I believe keeping my body well hydrated was key to avoiding the worst side effects of chemo. Mouth sores, in particular, are a real issue. I rinsed my mouth regularly with hydrogen peroxide, never varied from this process and did not experience any sores, which is a side-effect some chemo patients experience. I also avoided losing all my hair, thank God! I did experience thinning but never lost it all. I know this is not the most common experience, so I am grateful for that little victory!

Chemo days are taxing on so many levels. The anticipation sets in days prior, which robbed me of necessary rest. After the treatment was done, the remainder of my day was spent in complete rest; to allow the medications to work and my body to heal. I did require a sleep aid, and followed my oncologist's advice to take something to help me rest. I took steps to prepare myself mentally and physically for each treatment. I began and ended each day with Essiac tea, which my friend Bernie recommended to me. I did most of my treatments in the afternoon so, in the mornings, when I could, I would attend a yoga class. When chemo time rolled around, I was centered and strong for the treatment. I believed strongly that I had to keep my energy and emotions up in order to win the battle.

Whatever exercise or activity I could do to keep myself physically and emotionally sharp, I didn't let chemo block me from it. One side effect I experienced was chemo brain. I refer to it as feeling like I had mild confusion. Quite frankly, others noticed it more than I did.

One issue I struggled with during downtime after chemo was having to lean on others for support. I was terrified of being needy. I thought I'd appear weak. I realized though that I had to let myself rely on others.

There also comes the day during chemo when food and beverages begin to taste like metal.

Surviving and living with cancer is mysterious, no doubt, and demands reconstruction of our mind and body.

Reconstruction—our voice, not a doctor's choice

Whether or not a woman chooses to have surgical reconstruction is a personal decision. There are pro and con arguments on which choice is best. I listened to my heart and silenced the voice that harshly judged my desire—my need—to feel whole, healthy and beautiful inside and out. Breast implants are not the signature of a vain survivor any more than an artificial limb symbolizes the vanity of an amputee. Whatever body part may be missing, we all want to be whole. Whichever path we choose is indeed honorable and responding to and fighting breast cancer is in and of itself brave, period.

The sting of learning you have breast cancer in some ways immobilizes us and interferes with our ability to make decisions the way we normally would. I didn't follow my usual course to seek out the opinions of several doctors in choosing a surgeon. I had selected a highly recommended surgeon who I thought would do a great job but it was not going well and it was becoming a hindrance to my healing. Looking back, we didn't establish the level of communication I needed. I needed to be my assertive self during this process and I didn't allow myself to do that.

What followed for me, however, was a horrific experience. I never felt right after the post-mastectomy reconstruction. I never spoke up to the doctor about what I wanted, what I was comfortable with, what was safe. I was so frozen by the cancer diagnosis and what would happen next that I just let things happen. I let my caregivers, who knew me well, speak for me. I surrendered my voice, which complicated the process for me and for them. I picked the reconstructive surgeon based on recommendations and credentials. I chose a surgeon who did not understand my needs because we never discussed them. I didn't speak up and he followed his usual process. I share my story here as a cautionary tale, not as an argument against reconstruction. I did not speak up as I should have. I ended up having an expander inserted, did not heal well, and had too many scars.

Two doctors—two different planets

I wasn't feeling or looking the way I thought I should after three reconstructive surgeries. I ended up with different implants on each side. What should have looked like a natural breast, looked like a deformed football. I needed to look natural as possible, physically whole, and I needed to find a solution, someone who would hear me and help. Whether patients are suffering from breast cancer or exploring a preventative measure, breast reconstruction can be a daunting thought during a difficult time. Until now for me, it involved multiple surgeries with substandard results including multiple scars and an overall unnatural look. The original surgeon I chose was the only one I spoke with. He came highly recommended and had all the credentials you'd want your surgeon to have. I went into this process feeling it was the quickest path to feeling normal again. Immediately after my mastectomy, during the same surgery, I underwent breast reconstruction on my right breast. My surgeon undertook my procedure like a painter begins a painting. He saw a blank canvass upon which to create. He had met with me before the procedure to take measurements but we weren't conversing. I went silent as I listened to the surgeon explain his process.

After my reconstruction surgery, I was in pain. I expected that things would take some time but what I saw of the reconstructed breast was a mess. I questioned myself whether what I was seeing was not as it was supposed to be or if I was just being impatient with the process. Maybe what I was seeing in the mirror was all right and I just needed to give it all more time? Fighting cancer was my primary focus—chemotherapy was the next step and all the fears and anxiety around that were present. I felt what I needed to prepare for was being pushed aside by my reconstructive experience. My internal voice was telling me that the results of my reconstruction were less than satisfactory. I pushed that feeling down and chose to be positive, to let the process and my surgeon work.

Six months after I completed my chemo treatments, I began the steps to have my left breast removed. I knew early on this would be the eventual outcome. The second mastectomy and reconstructive surgery were almost a year to the day after the first. It did not improve the situation. I looked at myself physically and was shocked and further depressed. My optimism was fading. I was being reactionary, not proactive about my healing. I needed to ask questions but I wasn't. My reconstruction was not coming along as I hoped. I feared more surgery lay ahead. Coming out of chemo and now a new set of surgeries, I felt defeated and depressed.

Another surgery

I still was unhappy with how my body looked and felt after the second mastectomy (left side). I lived a healthy lifestyle, I work as a wellness consultant. How could I do that again if I was depressed about my body's condition? Every time I showered or got dressed there was the reminder that I was not whole. I contacted my friend, Paula, who had been diagnosed shortly after I was. I was struggling and I wanted to see how she was

44

doing so I called her immediately after my third surgery. She had been diagnosed and had surgery after me and appeared to be recovering much faster than I was. I had gone through three surgeries by this time. In addition to finding out how she was doing, I called to ask about her surgical team.

We hadn't spoken before about our respective journeys. As we talked, she explained that she had interviewed my surgical team and she was not comfortable with them. She recommended I speak with her reconstructive surgeon, Dr. Luis Viñas. I was tired of feeling crappy, of feeling like I was not right. So I made the call to Dr. Viñas and met with him within a couple of days.

My relationship with Dr. Viñas started with a *conversation.* I learned that he had spent many years developing techniques to bypass this traumatic series of surgeries I had gone through and had perfected a single-stage, immediate reconstruction that in most cases with the choice of a skin and nipple sparing option. I knew after I spoke with him that here was my ticket to feeling better.

What I learned in our conversation was that this revolutionary surgery is done in conjunction with your general surgeon during the mastectomy procedure. Everything is done in a single stage. You wake up with a fully reconstructed breast and no need for tissue expanders. Dr. Viñas uses a collagen product called SurgiMend®, which acts as a pocket for the implant. The product eventually incorporates with your own tissue and becomes totally replaced with collagen from your own body. This reconstruction process results in the most natural-looking breasts, sometimes enhancing and improving how the natural breasts were prior to surgery. Dr. Viñas' technique eliminates so much pain, confusion and time.

I was ready, after too many reconstructive procedures, to make space in my heart to welcome myself home again: a bit modified, but healthy, cancer-free and every bit a woman as I had been before.

I am humbled, as a cancer survivor, to be turning my setback into a comeback through the support of family, friends and the extraordinary medical team that stared into the face of this monster and said, "You Lose."

Life after cancer

I am now 4-years post diagnosis, 3-years post treatment. I feel physically and mentally stronger than I was before I knew I had cancer. While I would never wish cancer on someone, I appreciate that cancer gave me a chance to be a better person. I went through hell, and now I'm back, appreciating life and my relationships. I've adapted to change and come through stronger. The life of a survivor is one of ever-vigilance for the monster's return but I put my energy into being prepared and persevering. I did the work to survive and I want to help others to do the same. I've earned my survivorship and I will do anything to maintain it. It's a choice to make, and an effort to take. If you mentally go down, you physically go down, there is no plan B!

CЯ ВЭ

Photos

Your attitude and the choices you make
today, will be your life tomorrow.

— Unknown

"There are only two ways to live your life. One is as though nothing is a miracle. The other is as though everything is a miracle."

— Albert Einstein

"Sometimes the questions are complicated and the answers are simple."

—Dr. Seuss

"You should *have* an experience;
it shouldn't just *be* an experience."

— Alan Cumming

Life always offers you a second chance.
It's called tomorrow.

—Nicholas Sparks

Don't talk, just act. Don't say, just show. Don't promise, just prove.

— Unknown

I've learned that people will forget what you said, will forget what you did, but people will never forget how you made them feel.

— Maya Angelou

It's not *what* we have in life, but *who* we have in our life that matters.

— J.M. Laurence

Live fully, love deeply,
let go with no bitterness."

— Paulo Coelho

Life isn't about waiting for the storm to pass,
it's about learning to dance in the rain.

— Vivian Greene

Life is 10% of what you make it
and 90% of how you take it.

— Irving Berlin

LIVE LIKE crazy

Part Two—Lead Your Life, Don't Chase it

What lies behind us and what lies ahead are tiny matters compared to what lies within us.

— Henry Stanley Haskins,
***Meditations in Wall Street* (W.Morrow, 1940)**

Hearing the words, "You've got cancer," is a shock-and-awe moment in our lives, even if you suspected it was true before you were tested, as I did. And to be frank, when you get that diagnosis, there isn't much awe. Cancer almost always evokes a fear response in people. No one I know or have ever heard about has ever high-fived their doctor upon hearing that sentence. What I want people to know is that it is the start of a process, which I call the cancer journey. It becomes a date-time stamp in your life history, you BC (before cancer), you after.

My purpose in this section of the book is to help patients, their families and caregivers walk a mile in the shoes of someone who has been there so that they may learn, gain insights and possibly prepare themselves for what is coming. You've read about my experience, my cancer journey, but one cancer patient's story does not make a full picture. Here I am drawing on my personal experience as well as those of the numerous patients and friends for whom I have helped as a patient advocate. These are people I have counselled through the process, helped find clarity in their decision making, gain understanding about their journey and what's coming.

I hope this book helps you take the very next step on the journey; to not let the initial shock and fear that follows paralyze you. This is a time for courage, to walk through the fear, each step, one following the other. I want to help you get past that shock and fear and to take action. With action comes healing. In part one, my story, I focused on my journey with breast cancer. While each type of cancer is its own unique disease, the path to healing following traditional medicine is largely the same, Usually surgery, then radiation (if appropriate), followed by chemotherapy. Working with a board-certified oncologist, together you'll determine a treatment plan, with a timeline detailing each step. For me it was surgery followed by chemotherapy. Due to my particular type of breast cancer, poorly differentiated, Stage 2, ductile carcinoma, radiation was not appropriate for the plan. But for many patients, the process follows logical, predictable steps barring experiencing any infection or irregular vital signs.

I have created a list of coaching points to help patients navigate those steps. They do not follow a particular order and are applicable at many steps of the process. With each coaching point, I am sharing an exercise to help you put the coaching into action. There is a popular aphorism in coaching that it takes 21 days to turn a new action into a habit. In 21 days you can eliminate a negative behavior by replacing it with a positive one. The exercises I'm sharing are aimed to help you find a positive habit coming through the other side of your cancer fight. A focus on the positive turns cancer from a difficult, life-threatening fight into a life-affirming journey, so that you can *Live Life Crazy!*

Coaching for Cancer Survivors

The bad news—you've been diagnosed with cancer.

The good news—more people than ever before are surviving it.

I do not mean to be glib with that little couplet. As I said earlier, I am positive to a fault. While getting a cancer diagnosis is certainly bad news, there is every reason to hope, to be optimistic, that you will be OK!

A 2015 study in California looked at all new cancer diagnoses (over 155,000 cases) over a 25-year period (1988-2012) in the San Francisco region and determined that rates of cancer have dropped more than 13 percent overall, which they attribute largely to the decline in smoking-related cancers. That's good news. More importantly, the study determined that mortality rates for the patients they tracked have declined for all cancer types in all racial/ethnic groups and for both genders by an average of 1.8% per year from 1995 through 2012, which closely matches the national figure of a 1.5 percent decline annually over the same period.

"So what?" you ask. "OK, cancer is on the decline, but I still got it." After diagnosis, the first thing most patients want to know is, "Will I live?" Today, the fight against cancer is winnable. Yes, loved ones are still dying, but that heartbreaking outcome is becoming less and less common. When we are diagnosed, we are drafted into a space that at times is beyond our control, yet we need to give ourselves permission to be comfortable with the information we gather, the choices we need to make, the professionals we rely on, and the support we receive. Focusing on these things, pushing past the fear, will lead you to healing. For the vast majority of patients today, the cancer journey is no longer a dead-end street.

OK, What's Next?

That is another common question for people in our shoes. The answer though is as varied as the people who have been diagnosed with cancer. My guess is that most people, like myself, want to read everything they can get their hands on related to cancer and its treatments. Others reach out and seek the advice of those who have walked in their shoes, seeking inspirational stories to give them hope—if she beat it, I can, too!

Yes, there are moments when we feel hopeful, sensing that if we beat cancer, we get a do-over, a second chance to do it all better. There will also be other times when we are filled with anger. Feeling depressed and that your world is spinning out of control is normal, but don't invest a minute gauging your sanity. Please take the time to understand your feelings. Our immediate response is as unique as we each are and just as important.

Our first response is not the only response we will have. In time, if we allow ourselves to process what is going on inside physically and emotionally and out—telling family and friends, scheduling and keeping appointments, talking with doctors and caregivers—we begin to connect and engage with others, hear their voices of experience, and we may even find we are learning positive and valuable things. Our response to each step on the journey is affected by our energy, our attitude and our general health. Taking additional steps to focus on those items will guide your responses.

What happens now is you begin the process of healing. You've been given a preliminary diagnosis and now medical science kicks into high gear. You'll begin a battery of tests to determine what type of cancer you have. Be assured that it's critically important to accurately diagnose what type of cancer you have and where it is in order to treat it properly. As I noted earlier, cancer is not one disease, it is a family of diseases. The cellular mutation process is basically the same but the treatments are not. The characteristics of the tumor, such as its size, location, growth rate and if it has spread to nearby areas (metastasized), affects the particulars of each person's treatment plan. In general, it's best to accept and to not lose sight of the many different types of tumors, their shapes and sizes; each diagnosis is likely unique in the scheme of things. As you learn more and share information with others, be aware that other people and patients will want to help you by sharing their diagnosis and journey, or their family member's and friends'. Their efforts are intended to be empathetic but theirs is not your story. Try to avoid relating those stories' and their details to your own. You are unique, your cancer is unique and your treatment will be unique.

Your doctor orders a battery of tests, which depend upon the type of cancer you have. It may be blood work, a mammogram, MRI, CAT, PET or ultrasound, which examine our tissue from outside, or more invasive tests like colonoscopy or a biopsy to extracts a small sample of effected tissue or fluid to analyze the tumor cells microscopically. This is not an all-inclusive list but know that your doctor is trying to gather as much information as she or he possibly can. Each test evaluates something different and gives your medical team more insight into how your type of cancer works, its strength and weaknesses and how it can be attacked, all to hone in on the best treatment options. While it is always good to ask questions, to learn more about what is happening to you, don't question or resist the plan your doctor recommends. They are working from an extensive knowledge base that has been tested and has evolved with each case they have treated. If an additional exam or test will assist in detecting anything suspicious, be receptive and value your doctor's need to thoroughly investigate your case—we ultimately benefit from their diligence!

There are three standard treatment options for most patients: surgery, radiation and chemotherapy. There are alternative and complementary treatments, which can be discussed with your doctor. For the vast majority of patients, their treatment plan may include all three or a combination of one or two of these standard treatments.

Surgery generally removes the cancer from your body, but it doesn't always get rid of it all. Sometimes a tumor encroaches into surrounding tissue. Chemotherapy cleans your body systemically of any remaining cancerous cells. It may be done prior to surgery or radiation treatment or after. Chemo is a toxic mix of medicines that attacks the mutant cancer cells in your body. It poisons them, which they cannot recover from as your healthy cells do. It affects every part of your body; it literally hits you from head to toe, inside and out. Think of it as hitting the restart on your immune system. During the course of treatment, chemo patients have to be watchful for infections as their white blood cells, the work horses of the immune system, are compromised. While undergoing chemotherapy, your medical team pays close attention to your T-cells, a type of white blood cell. If a patient's T-cell count is too low, their risk of contracting contagious diseases or infections increases.

Radiation is also a common course of treatment for many patients. Radiation targets a specific site where the cancer grew to attack cancer cells. It may be performed without other treatments, before surgery to reduce the size of a tumor, or after surgery to eliminate any cancer-effected cells that may not have been removed during surgery. In some cases, like mine, there is no radiation therapy.

We are each one of the many people who have been diagnosed with cancer. Hearing a doctor say, "You have cancer." is indescribably deafening. Not anything we ever expect to hear in our lifetime, yet we are not alone. There are many people facing this beast, just like us, it's predicted that more 1 million people are diagnosed annually in the US.

We have all cried, been challenged by choices, felt angry and eventually laughed again. I promise.

I'm sharing this message by writing this book to share my wisdom with you. I want to help make your journey a little easier. Draw on my strength and the support of family, friends, caregivers and medical teams with extraordinary skill and a level of compassion that rises far above our needs and expectations. Oh, I know, too well, at first it feels overwhelming, like you're caught in a wild fire.

Yet in time, you will know firsthand the value of actively planning your treatment and life ahead.

Try not to allow yourself to be overwhelmed. My purpose—my passion—is to inspire and guide you to be your own best advocate, to be the gatekeeper of your life. Because no one else can take care of us as well as we can.

What follows in the next pages are my coaching points, which I offer you, my fellow travelers on your cancer journey as guideposts. I hope that my book will help guide you through the hills and valleys on your healing path, and will help you feel that you are not alone.

At the end of each coaching point, I offer you an insight from another fellow traveller who has made the journey. I asked my friends to summarize their journey in one word, which I am sharing here with their blessing. Following each coaching tip is an exercise or an activity to help you focus on that positive insight, to ease your journey, to smooth your healing path.

Be your own advocate

An enlightened person doesn't ask someone to believe anything. They simply point the way and leave others to experience it for themselves.

We should never forget that education means communication, and communication is the exchange of ideas. Regardless of the treatment plan your medical team prescribes, I encourage all cancer patients to focus their attention and energy into their healing process while the medical team concentrates on eliminating the cancer. There are many steps patients can take to maximize their healing that complements their medical treatment. I mentioned before that I am a life coach. I work with individuals to help them to identify and focus on what they need to do, what actions they need to take, to remove the obstacles to their success. I give my clients objective advice and help them make informed decisions for themselves, decisions that fear sometimes prevents them from making.

Today, I apply the same coaching process and principles when working with cancer patients. The coaching points I am giving you here are meant to complement what you and your doctor are doing medically to treat your cancer, it does not replace sound medical treatment. What we can control is our level of fear. I am here as a cancer survivor to tell you that fear is cancer's ally.

When fear paralyses patients, cancer wins.

I intend my coaching points to help you put yourself in a stronger position to work with your medical team to achieve the best possible outcome, short term and long. We know cancer can be beaten. I did, others in my family have, my friends have. I believe you can beat it too!

The coaching I am offering to you summarizes my personal experience along with those of my family, friends, their friends and many other patients I've been in contact with in fighting this horrid disease. I want to give each cancer patient, each caregiver, each person touched by it in some way, the power and will to fight cancer.

At the end of the day, you only need to be satisfied with the performance of one person— *you*. Be bold enough to concentrate on you and the answers will come from within. Be realistic and practical when it comes to your emotions.

Annie ~ Empowered

Healing exercise:

Research your treatment plan. Ask your doctor if there are options to enhance your treatment. It's okay to look at alternatives like holistic treatments to find the plan that works for you—this is the time for your due diligence, to investigate what options are best for you. What options can augment your treatment plan? What are the success rates of standard treatments? Alternative treatments?

Review your treatment plan and have an honest and frank conversation with your internist/GP about other things you can be doing to support your healing. Statistics say the most successful treatments are a combination of the primary treatments—surgery, radiation and chemotherapy. But there are certainly many things we can do spiritually, nutritionally, physically and emotionally to maximize and support our own healing journey. Educate yourself on those options, have conversations with experts. What things are you comfortable doing?

The choice is yours, own it!

Be bold, take action

> *Inaction breeds doubt and fear.*
> *Action breeds confidence and courage.*
> *If you want to conquer fear, do not sit*
> *home and think about it.*
> *Go out and get busy.*
> —Dale Carnegie

My mission, my hope, is that the experiences and the views shared in this book speak and deliver a strong dynamism that gives people the courage to change. Change requires boldness, a willingness to stop what was, and to begin what will be. For cancer patients, doing nothing, riding it out, is a poor choice for survival. Cancer does not stop; it does not care, it just keeps eating at you. Saving your life depends upon taking action as early as possible.

The first action to take after you've learned you have been diagnosed with cancer is to breathe. Breath equals life. We humans can go days without water, weeks without food, years without companionship, but life lasts but minutes without breathing. The first step on the journey is to breathe.

Yes, I understand this sounds overly simple. But your healing journey requires you to take time for yourself. We are all too busy running here and there, focused on our work, school, kids, followed by even more work, more school. Yes, you are needed, and though it may seem as if the world will crash into the Sun if you stop for a bit, believe me when I tell you it won't. I saw in my own journey and in those of many friends and acquaintances, who I helped through this process, the world went on, it didn't miss a spin. However, your world may end if you don't stop to take a breath. If ever there was a time to make time for you, this is it. It's now time to stop thinking of "me-time" as being selfish. You must make it a necessity and a priority.

Breathing relaxes the body and clears the mind. It is to be sure a tense situation. Many people react with fear, some with disbelief, and others with anger. If that first step for the patient is to breathe, that opens the door to the next healing steps. Be bold and be prepared to take the steps you and your medical team choose. Fight the fear you are feeling and begin the journey.

Hey, don't think they cut the cancer out of our bodies and it's done. We also need to cut the cancer out of our minds, too. We have to live, eat and breathe with positive intention. Choose to focus on the healing not the cancer. Each step in your journey must be about healing you. Cancer brings opportunity for reflection and introspection, which is not necessarily a bad thing, as long as we ask ourselves the right questions. Search for and realize the beauty of serenity—this is important. Find every means of healing that speaks to you and throw it at the disease in your body. It's not enough to get up and walk it off. You need to pray, meditate, exercise, eat, rest, play, talk, laugh and hug it out.

Approach each day with a sense of calm and don't allow periods of pressure and chaos to control you. There is always something to be done; focus on the task at hand and do your best to move forward each day.

Gloria ~ Gratitude

Healing exercises:

1) Answer the following questions regarding taking time for yourself:

- What will it take to make time for you a priority?

- What is keeping you from doing the things that inspire and energize you?

- What activities do you enjoy and will nurture you?

- How can you change and take enjoyment in doing these things?

2) Now, list three things you might do differently with this "second chance" at life. Identify two or more action steps you can take for each item to make this change happen. Be realistic. I'm not advocating that you act irresponsibly. Think of things that you wish you could do or want to do but haven't. Think simple. Is it someone you need to visit, perhaps a relative you haven't seen or spoken with? Take a class to finish a degree or just for fun?

Now for each item, set a time goal to complete the actions (example, by September 15, I will...). Then go out and do it!

Ask questions, make choices

It is very easy for cancer patients to sit back and just say yes to what we are being told. There is an avalanche of information to absorb and much of it is highly technical. For me, contrary to my character, I clammed up. My doctor would ask me a question and when I didn't respond, and my loving husband answered. Bless him; he was trying to take care of me. What I needed to do, however, was to speak up, to tell the doctors how I felt, what I needed. This can be a difficult hurdle for some people, I get it. Whether we are respectfully deferring to the judgement of medical professionals, or listening to the advice and instructions of caregivers, we need to be ready with questions: "Do I take this medicine with or without food?" "Will this make me groggy?" "Will my hair fallout?" If it is important to you, ask it! No question is out of bounds. And just as important, if you don't understand the answer, ask for clarification—keep asking until you understand. No one expects you to understand the cellular biology of a cancer cell, but you probably will in time.

Try to think of your treatment as an extended conversation with the medical team and your caregivers. This team has come together to rally around you. You must step up and engage the team in the conversation, which you are the cen-

78

ter of. Start conversations again and again. It's not selfish or self-centered to permit yourself to be the focus of discussion. In fact, it is necessary for your healing. When I was undergoing treatment, I was not speaking up for myself. There were questions I needed to ask, things I needed to ask for. My healing went off-track for a time because I was not engaged in the conversation. Once I found my voice, once I spoke up, my healing path became clear and I made progress.

Beth ~ Grateful

Healing exercise:

This is an important exercise to focus on. For some people asking questions comes naturally. They want to know the who, what, why, when, where and how all the time. For other patients, this means stepping out of their comfort zone. The exercise is fairly simple and helps patients who are most reluctant to ask questions. Keep a writing pad with you for every doctor appointment and every therapy treatment. Make a list of questions to ask and to whom you want to ask them. Patients often feel muted by our doctor's knowledge and expertise, and forget the questions we want and need to ask when we are sitting in an exam room. By keeping a pad with your list of questions, you can capture them as they occur. In this exercise, you are taking ownership for your treatment. Asking questions lets your medical team know that you are engaged and prepared for your journey, you've done your homework and are ready to get down to the business of healing. You have taken a measure of control over the things that you can. Then, with your list of questions on-hand, ask them, and keep asking them, until you get the answers you understand. If this becomes a pattern, your medical team will become used to the fact that you are prepared to ask questions and they will be better prepared to spend time answering them for you.

Keep in mind that by asking questions, you are engaging in your treatment. Getting answers and explanations helps you make decisions that are best for you.

Understand, not judge

Be understanding of caregivers and medical professionals. They are working with you, being sensitive to your needs but they are human, too. They deal with multiple cases each day, some are heart-breaking at the same time that other patients are celebrating milestones on their journey. They will have good days and bad just like you but they typically will put that aside to focus on you. A friend underwent treatment for thyroid cancer. As part of the treatment, the patient must be isolated for a period of time, three to ten days, from family and loved ones, due to the lasting effects of the radiation treatment. For this friend, that was extremely uncomfortable. Her meals had to be brought to her, she was isolated from her children. Her discomfort with the isolation spilled over to being cranky about being cared for. Cranky turned to complaining, which made caring for her more difficult.

Here the Golden Rule applies. Try to see yourself through the eyes of your caregivers. Gain perspective on how you are as a patient. Ask them for what you need and remember that kindness goes a long way. They will feel better about caring for you, and you will feel better, period!

Paula ~ Understanding

Healing exercise:

You know this joke:

Q. How many psychiatrists does it take to change a light bulb?

A. None, the light bulb has to want to change.

Understanding others can be a difficult thing to master. You can completely understand some people, understand most people a little, and a few you'll never get. Regardless, that does not mean we do not have to work on it. I love the Michael Jackson song "Man in the Mirror." The only person you can change is yourself. You may influence others, guide them, teach them how to treat you, but the actual change is theirs. And that is the center piece of this exercise. Have a conversation with yourself in a mirror. Ask yourself, what can you do better to understand this other person, whether it is your doctor, a loved one, or another caregiver. How can you show them appreciation and gratitude for their position? What too, can you do to help them understand you, what you are feeling, what you need, so that they can care for you in a positive way, one that promotes your healing.

Be charitable

I see daily stresses in greater perspective. Being able to dedicate my energy to the needs of cancer patients and their healing allows me to shift my focus from myself, my issues and problems to how I can use my experience and insights to help others on their cancer journey. As a survivor, I speak the language of gratitude daily, and my commitment to share my experiences and to write this book has awakened a euphoric feeling that I have grabbed hold of and speak to with tremendous thanksgiving. Take this opportunity to dedicate some energy to the needs of others. The energy you give creates a feedback loop that ricochets energy back to you. It enhances the positive energy the universe sends in your direction.

Giving to others is good for your body, mind and soul. I'm not just saying this, science backs me up! When we give to others, our body releases feel-good chemicals into the brain, endorphins. These endorphins promote positive energy, mood and healing in the body. Endorphins are natural pain killers that improve mood and stimulate the body's immune system, two things that are positive for any cancer patient. Happiness is not just the mood we choose, it is a chemical condition created by the release of endorphins. Endorphins work like the opiate drugs codeine and morphine but without the negative addictive side effects.

Carol ~ Thankful

Healing exercise:

We all have something to give: our time, talent or treasure. For the purposes of this exercise, it can be any one of those three things.

People who volunteer tend to have higher self-esteem, psychological well-being, and happiness. All of these things go up as feelings of social connectedness goes up, which in reality, it does. It also improves their health and even their longevity."
—Phillip Moeller, US News

Personally, I think time is the most valuable thing we have to give, and the one that gives back the most. Here, I want you to create a giving tree. Think of the tree as your life, with different branches for your family, friends, community, and whatever else you can commit to. On those branches will hang leaves you will make from post-its. Take several post-it notes and write one item on each. These items will be things you can give to that branch. Examples could include reading to children at the local library, volunteer at an animal shelter, create a scholarship fund, or host a neighborhood get together. You get the idea; do what you can do. Make them simple projects that you can commit to doing, projects that feed your energy, not ones that drain it.

Honor yourself

As adults, especially as parents, we often find it difficult to place our needs ahead of our family's. This may be a generational thing for middle-aged adults who were taught that being selfish was bad; it was a dishonorable trait. While I get that, I knew my healing would come with a new set of circumstances. I had to begin asking myself to listen to my intuitions with a sense of openness, not fear. I had to be in-tune with myself, even a little selfish. I had to prioritize my feelings, I needed to listen to them as cues and signals that spoke to where I was and what I needed. I really do believe that pain and challenges are a sign of growing, and when we are suddenly gentle with ourselves, we generate the same energy in others.

Vulnerability, too, is a breeze when we love ourselves. Think about it. When we are not completely comfortable with ourselves, we guard our insecurities and create space between us. We create a defensive barrier around our vulnerabilities as wide as the ocean, but we need all the courage we can gather to swim across. With vulnerability, truly allowing ourselves to be vulnerable to others in our lives, we experience true connection—respect for ourselves and others—and we then attract others who are inspired by our openness. I encourage everyone to show your complexities, to let others in to see your weaknesses so that they might better support you. You will be pleasantly surprised how loving and respecting ourselves and sharing this with others will connect us with everyone.

I experienced this with my reconstructive surgery. Not until I opened up and showed my family how deeply affected I was by what I felt was a poorly done, poorly managed process, did I create space to find a better solution. They saw my moodiness and depression but not what was behind it. At that point, I reached out to my friend Paula about her journey. I knew that her recovery had progressed much better than mine and I needed to let myself open up to her. Until I pushed through the walls of fatigue, depression and fear to let everyone be more aware of my feelings, was I able to look for a new solution. I had to open a conversation with them about what I needed and to find a doctor I trusted who heard me. By being focused on your needs, and honest about them, you gain clarity on the next steps to take.

Bernie ~ Casual vs Casualty

Healing exercise:

List three things that you need to do just for you. For each one, rate them on a scale of 1 to 5 (1 is lowest, 5 is highest) how important they are for your physical, mental and spiritual wellbeing. As you think about a number to assign, think about what the cost to you is if it is not done. Now, add the other items on your to-do list and rate them. Are any of your personal items a 5 and others are not? Honoring yourself in part means making your needs as much a priority as those of others in your life.

Love: Enjoy friends, cherish family

Without question more than anything else, cancer has strengthened my view and value of our human connection. Human kindness means so much more than material things. I now know that the human spirit can overcome and soar above adversity; every negative becomes a positive, and tremendous strength is revealed when we embrace it. I now try to live each day fully, not wishing for or relying on tomorrow, which after all is not a given.

You will come to rely on many people during your cancer journey. Some friends and family might shrink away. Try not to take this personally. Cancer is just as frightening for them as it is for you and people who shrink away are uncomfortable with their emotions about your situation. That's on them, not you. At the same time, an amazing miracle will occur. People you love and care for will step up. They will plant themselves by your side and be your wingman on your cancer journey. For me this was my husband, sister and cousin. I did not take a step on my journey without one of them being with me. When I was not strong, they carried me. When I was, they let me walk. If I learned one thing from cancer, it is to cherish those people who are closest to you, who will carry you when you need it most.

Cynthia ~ Life

Healing exercise:

There is a wonderful exercise about understanding your priorities, presented by Stephen Covey in his book First Things First, which illustrates this idea beautifully. I'll summarize it here but you can look this up on YouTube, Google or other places.

A speaker stands at the front of the room with a clear container in front of her. Out of view of the audience are three full containers. She takes a container full of large baseball-sized stones and pours it into the empty container. She looks up and asks the people watching her if her bucket appears full. Most people nod or speak that yes, the container looks full. She picks up another of the out-of-sight containers and begins pouring pebbles over the larger stones. These pebbles fill in the spaces around the larger stones. The speaker asks again if the container is full. Now, more people agree that it is full. The speaker brings up a third container full of sand and begins pouring the sand into the container of stones and pebbles. The sand filters down through the container. "Is the container full?" the presenter asks? The audience agrees, now, the container is full. The speaker takes a pitcher of water and pours it into the container full of rocks, pebbles and sand. The water easily washes around the other items and fills the container.

With the container now full, the speaker explains, the container is a metaphor for our lives. We need to be careful in what order we fill our containers. The biggest stones represent the most important things in our lives: family, health, faith. The pebbles represent other important things, like work and friends. The sand and water represents all the other things that fill our days, busy schedules, emails, etc.

If we fill the container with the less important things first, there will not be enough room for the most important things. Fill your buckets with big important things, and let the little things flow around them.

Be grateful, always smile

My life before cancer required a zoom lens that I focused on the many details of things: where I had to be, who I had to see, what had to be done and in what order. My life was always moving at a frenzied pace. Today, I work on slowing down and taking my time to look at the landscape around me. I try to think before I act. Life after cancer now is nothing short of panoramic.

As a survivor, I speak the language of gratitude daily, yet the commitment to share my experience and write this book has awakened a euphoric feeling that I have grabbed hold of and speak to with tremendous thanksgiving. I have learned in my cancer journey to be grateful for my family, friends and experiences that could have been taken away from me. Eleanor Roosevelt is often quoted as saying, "Yesterday is history. Tomorrow is a mystery. But today is a gift, which is why it is called the Present." I like how this so beautifully teaches us to be grateful for the time we have.

I am thankful to cancer for one thing. It has given me a chance to be a better person, to be Sally 2.0, a better version of myself before cancer. Now I have an attitude of gratitude, taking note of the things that make me happy, that make me smile.

I better appreciate the blessings of my life. I feel the stress of schedules and goals less acutely and enjoy experiences more.

Joan ~ Gratitude

Healing exercise:

This exercise is an easy one that we often forget to do when we are running madly through our lives. It takes but a few moments of reflection each day. Here's how it works. Get a notebook with enough paper that you can keep a daily journal for a few months. Each day for the first two weeks of your journey, list three things that were the best part of your day. Briefly identify why this was a best part of your day. These need not be life-altering experiences or bucket-list type things; keep it simple and close to you (example: went for a walk, shared time with a friend, enjoyed some quiet time outdoors).

Starting the third week, add one more item. Then continue adding one more item with each new week. As you continue the exercise, you'll find it easier and easier to identify gratifying things around you. Your gratitude antennae will become more fine-tuned to the little things that you might have missed before. With each week, focusing on these positive things will enhance the healing energy around you, sustaining you in the difficult days.

Zen and the art of personal maintenance

Work hard, play harder—Cancer teaches us to use our time wisely, productively. Energy-draining things need to be put on hold. Energy-building activities need to become priorities. This can be your work, for some people pour themselves into their jobs because it gives them a level of satisfaction and accomplishment.

With that being said, I think there needs to be time for play. Is this time to check off those bucket list items? Maybe you can; it depends upon your level of energy and ability to manage your care commitments. Who would want to take a trip to the Grand Canyon just to sit in a hotel sick, drained of energy? Be honest with yourself about what you can manage.

For me, I kept a regular work-out routine. I attended yoga classes frequently. Often on chemo days, I would be in a yoga class in the morning then have chemo in the afternoon. Then I went home and rested. It worked for me without overtaxing my body.

Take walks—Moderate physical activity during treatment is an important element of healing. I think walking is a great, low-impact exercise that keeps the body limber, the heart pumping and the mind clear. And, barring any prior disability, we can all walk. No training is needed, no special equipment is required, you just get up and go!

Along with the physical activity, taking a walk exercises the mind. It helps us to actively process the day ahead or just completed in a way that sitting and thinking (inactive processing) cannot duplicate. Walking along a garden path or through a park helps us concentrate. The increased heart rate helps thinking and concentration. A University of Illinois study showed the link between moderate exercise, like walking, and the positive effect it has on concentration.

If you want to do more than walk, for example if you are a runner and want to continue that exercise, it would be best to discuss this with your doctor how far you can push your body. Remember that a slower pace is not giving in, it is helping your body heal.

Rest—Regular rest is an investment in your health. The human body uses its rest periods to heal; it is when your immune system does its best work. Allow yourself healing time. Make sure you have a set sleep schedule, which may include daily naps. During my chemo treatment days, coming home and resting allowed me to function better the next day. It wasn't that I was incapable of functioning after chemo, I rested so that I functioned better the next day, so I felt OK—not great but just OK. Each day between chemo sessions is your time for recharging and healing in preparation for your next session.

Regina ~ Patience

Healing exercise:

Winston Churchill was an expert napper. His nation was at war for its survival yet he blocked out time for a nap each day. It's wasn't because he was old, tired and needed rest to handle the rigors of his day. No he napped because he felt it gave him the energy to do two days' worth of work in one. He explained:

You must sleep some time between lunch and dinner, and no half-way measures. Take off your clothes and get into bed. That's what I always do. Don't think you will be doing less work because you sleep during the day. That's a foolish notion held by people who have no imagination. You will be able to accomplish more. You get two days in one, well, at least one and a half, I'm sure. When the war started, I had to sleep during the day because that was the only way I could cope with my responsibilities.

You are fighting your own war now; it's also a war for survival. Like Churchill, you need rest in order to keep your wits about you, in order to defeat the enemy within. Set a rest-sleep schedule and keep to it each day. Healing occurs when the body is at rest. "Slow and steady," says the Tortoise, "wins the race."

Talk, listen & share

Speak up, it's our right and it only helps! When talking with caregivers, share EVERY side effect you are experiencing. It's important information your medical team needs to evaluate your condition. This is not the time to tough it out—you aren't whining. There are medications that can help address the pain, nausea, fatigue, restlessness or other symptoms and side effects you are feeling. If it's interfering with your life, speak up.

My post-chemo reconstructive surgeries went on for a full year until I finally met with a surgeon my friend, Paula, suggested. I never felt that my reconstruction looked good, and it did not feel good, either. I wanted to look and feel normal. I could not shake the thought from my mind. I had to do something as my healing was not progressing the way I thought it should. I saw Paula seemed to be back to normal much faster than me. When I reached out to her, it was with a sense of relief that I heard her story. She had interviewed a few breast cancer surgeons, including my team. She chose a different team than I had. Hearing her due diligence validated for me that what I was feeling wasn't just in my head. When I met Paula's surgeon, Dr. Viñas, we began with a *conversation*. I spoke to what I was feeling, and what I needed. He was receptive to what I had to say. Then, I listened to what he explained could be done to correct my previous reconstruction surgeries.

Once I reclaimed my voice, I was able to take control of the decisions I needed to make. Before our conversation, my healing time seemed like an endless journey. With Dr. Viñas, I felt for the first time, that there was a finish line. I could get back to what I felt like physically and emotionally.

Patti ~ Empathy

Healing exercise:

Many of us don't want to appear pushy, aggressive or rude, so we often don't speak up when we need to. In terms of your care, silence is not golden. Like it or not, you are the leader of your team. *Team You* needs a strong vocal leader. In this exercise, I want you to make a bulletpoint presentation for your next doctor appointment. Think of four to six items your doctor must know before you leave the exam room. Then write them down.

Think about the facility where you have chemo treatments. What could they do for you to make your experience there more pleasant? Would you choose a window seat or another spot where you would be most comfortable?

Now, write down those things that you would prefer and make it your job to ask. Along with sharing your needs is listening for the answer. Sometimes you will be accommodated, and sometimes you cannot. With the answer comes clarity. If you do not share your wants and needs, you are setting your team up for failure. And when it comes to *Team You* winning the battle against cancer, failure is not an option!

Serenity prayer (adapted version):

God, grant me the serenity to accept the people I cannot change,

The courage to change the one I can,

And the wisdom to know that one is me.

Explore & learn

Chemo brain is a real thing! I prefer to reference it as mild confusion. Quite frankly, others noticed it when I had it more than I.

Every patient is issued a list of POSSIBLE side effects they may experience, I emphasize POSSIBLE. It is good to be aware of each of them, but do not anticipate suffering from all or any of these side effects. Medications are available to address any side effects you may experience. Receive this as information only. Take the necessary steps to protect yourself from each. The first step is to communicate with your doctor. Be informed to make smart choices.

This list of symptoms is most terrifying to every survivor who contacts me immediately after diagnosis. I cannot emphasize enough that if you follow these suggestions you'll avoid some side effects. The list is a preventative measure, not a guaranteed journey.

Converse with your doctors, they are focused professionals working on the disease, not necessarily on the patient's needs. Identifying your needs (explore) and learning strategies to address them will pay you dividends through your healing time. For example, drink plenty of water. Start beginning the day before chemo. Do the same the day of chemo, and for four or five days after. There are multiple benefits to picking up this routine. Chemo medications are filtered by the liver and are excreted through the kidneys. Flushing our body helps remove the toxins faster, and helps aid in digestion (keeping us regular), and hydrates our skin. Water keeps our veins plump and easier for infusion needles to be inserted. Oh, and be aware of the need to include fiber in your diet. Maintaining a balance is critically important—knowing what your body needs—for what your body needs is a responsibility every patient needs to take on. Granted nausea is nasty, yet, I can assure you that constipation and diarrhea are horrible symptoms, especially after everything that a day of chemo treatment takes from you.

Jennifer ~ Blessed

Healing exercise

The American Cancer Society recommends that cancer patients focus on having good nutrition during their treatment programs. They published a guide online to help patients determine their needs, in consultation with their doctor, so that through a proper diet, they can maximize their healing and minimize the negative side effects that sometimes accompanies treatment.

Our lives will change dramatically once diagnosed and treatment begins. Here are a couple of tips to help you prepare for treatment:[1]

- Your caregivers will want to help you with a variety of tasks, from taking care of the kids to walking the dog. Be prepared to let them in, to be grateful for their support. Their support is vital to getting through the year of treatment and recovery.

- Look at the tasks you manage with your family. During treatment it will be difficult to focus on these tasks efficiently. Reach out to family and friends about taking over these duties while you undergo treatment. Ongoing communication with them will reduce the stresses and frustrations you both will experience. If people offer to help, take them seriously.

1 Source: American Cancer Society Nutrition guidelines
http://www.cancer.org/acs/groups/cid/documents/
webcontent/002903-pdf.pdf

Embrace their kindness with gratitude. It will benefit your healing and your connection to them.

- Keep conversation with your caregivers open and ongoing. Caregivers need to know what you need from them and lacking direction may tend to overcommit or overreach. It will take understanding from both of you.

- Talk to your medical team about any concerns you have about eating. They can help you make diet changes that will help manage unpleasant side effects (constipation, weight loss, nausea) some patients experience. You may also want to meet with a nutritionist to help plan your meals.

Spend two weeks tracking what you eat and drink at each meal and how much. During treatment, and after, you may do better with several smaller meals, or frequent snacks between meals, rather than three larger meals each day. Eating properly, keeping hydrated and moderate exercise are good strategies to help maximize your healing.

Laugh & hug

Laughter truly is the best medicine, and hugs are a very close second. A Japanese geneticist, Kazuo Murakami, studies laughter as a stimulant that triggers energy inside a person's DNA, potentially helping cure diseases.

That's as close as we can get with today's technology to see if laughter really has medicinal value.

But I don't think we need a genetic scientist to tell us what common sense already does. Laughing makes you feel better. We'd all rather be around people laughing and having a good time than a humorless person who brings down a room. Remember the Debbie Downer skits from Saturday Night Live in the early 2000s? We can laugh at Rachel Dratch's comedic skills, making light of humorless people. As cancer patients, we need the boost that laughter brings.

In the course of researching for this book, I found a remarkable online university dedicated to the health benefits of laughter. L.O.U., the Laughter Online University, has multiple resources and training exercises to help you laugh more and better.

Hugs are just about the nicest thing you can give someone that costs you nothing. Just like laughter, hugs generate positive energy within the body. Endorphins rush the brain and fill you with good feelings.

Like laughter, hugs help reduce stress in the body. University of North Carolina psychologist Karen Grewen, has found in her study on hugging that participants who discussed stressful subjects after hugging for 20 seconds, did not have as marked a stress response (increased heart rate) as couples who had the same discussion without hugging. Grewen attributes this to the levels of the hormone oxytocin, which was higher among the couples who hugged. The blood pressure of subjects who didn't hug each other rose significantly more in the experiment than that of those who hugged on cue. Levels of the so-called stress hormone, cortisol, which can have damaging physical effects, dropped more markedly among women than men in measured hugging sessions.

This suggests that having a good laugh or hug before a stressful event, helps reduce the overall amount of stress you will experience. Now, who needs a hug?

Jody ~ Breathe

Healing exercise:

Here are two things to do each day during your journey. If you have access to the internet, Google your favorite comedian. I don't care who it is, whoever it is that makes you laugh. Spend 20 minutes watching their videos. There are lots of them online at YouTube or other websites. If you don't have a specific comedian, try a TV show that makes you laugh. Late-night TV shows like Jimmy Fallon's, Stephen Colbert's, or Jimmy Kimmel's are designed to help you wind down, relax and laugh at life.

Choose your favorite comedian or TV show and simply laugh. Spend 20 to 30 minutes each day watching and laughing. I won't fault you if you choose to do more.

Second is to give yourself a hug quota each day. Can you hug ten different people each day? If you need to, start with three hugs then work up. Give each person a real hug. Feel your arms grip them tightly. Feel theirs grip you. If you can do this for 21 days, you'll have developed a new, healthy habit. Try to hug at least a couple of casual acquaintances, too. Ask first, then give them a good hug. In a short time, I bet you will begin to get some repeat customers!

Be kind, forgive

Mother Teresa is credited with the following poem, written on the wall of her home in Calcutta, which expresses this point beautifully.

*People are often unreasonable, illogical
  and self-centered;
    Forgive them anyway.*

*If you are kind, people may accuse you of
  selfish, ulterior motives;
    Be kind anyway.*

*If you are successful, you will win some
  false friends and some true enemies;
    Succeed anyway.*

*If you are honest and frank, people may
  cheat you;
    Be honest and frank anyway.*

*What you spend years building, someone
  could destroy overnight;
    Build anyway.*

*If you find serenity and happiness, they
  may be jealous;
    Be happy anyway.*

*The good you do today, people will often
  forget tomorrow;
    Do good anyway.*

Give the world the best you have, and it
may never be enough;
Give the world the best you've got
anyway.

You see, in the final analysis, it is
between you and your God;
It was never between you and them
anyway.

Cancer is not an excuse to be unkind. It takes great energy to deal with all that cancer takes from us, people around us see that. But at the same time, we can use our energy productively, lovingly. Treat caregivers with kindness. After all, they're the ones who have stepped up to help us.

Being angry about being struck with cancer is a natural response. Anger is one of the stages of grief. And to heal and move on, we must resolve that anger. Being angry at cancer, at God, at your family, at me for writing this book, is understandable for a time, but don't unpack and live there. Holding on to negative emotions of fear, anger, resentment, all drain you of energy, energy that is needed elsewhere. Forgiveness is a healing emotion. Its letting go of a helium-filled balloon and watching it float higher and farther away. Forgiveness liberates us from carrying about the baggage (negative emotions) and leaves us free to walk the journey ahead focused on healing.

Hey, we can't just cut the cancer out of us, have surgery and/or treatment and think we are done. We need to cut the cancer out of our minds, too. We have to live, eat and breathe with positive intention. Choose to forgive so that the healing can take place. Search for and realize the beauty of serenity—this is important—find every means of healing that speaks to you and throw it at the disease in your body.

Kim ~ Forward

Healing exercise

There's an old adage that says carrying around a grudge is like taking poison expecting the other person will die.

Kindness and forgiveness release negative energy from our bodies. If you are carrying anger or resentment toward someone, for some reason, or even at just getting sick, it is time to release that negative energy. It blocks your efforts to heal, so let go of it, and get your life back.

Kindness, like laughter discussed before, fills the spirit with positive, healing energy. Your exercise here it to build a list of kind acts you can complete, perhaps donating things people need. Visit a sick friend or relative. Do something random, like leave $5 gift cards on windshields at the grocery store.

It doesn't take much to build the positive healing energy you need to keep yourself moving forward!

Be strong

The biggest gap between success and failure is the willingness to try, the willingness to test ourselves. Our lives are simply a reflection and flow of who we are, what we do and where we've been. Not expected, breast cancer is never a welcome guest in our lives, yet its presence has taught me over time that the unexpected can give new meaning to our lives. I needed to shed the stress I placed on being organized and to give greater trust to letting things happen naturally. Before cancer, self-discipline and routine owned me. After cancer, I learned to put trust in chance for a change, to see the universe for what it is, and to stop fighting to control it. I can't, you can't; it's just too big! Now, I'm taking a bigger bite out of life and putting my trust in letting things happen naturally.

I am humbled to be healthy and alive, today. This life is a gift, every day is a gift. Our ability to achieve does not define us; success does not define us. It's our ability to love and be compassionate to others, using whatever gifts God has given us that defines each of us. So, do what you can while focusing on what's important. I'm learning with practice to stop talking long enough to really hear what others have to say—we've been given two ears and one mouth, so we should listen twice as much as we speak. When we invite others to share their fears, concerns—their stories—we all benefit and feed off of this feeling, a renewed sense of mutual respect and enthusiasm.

Since my diagnosis, treatment and surgeries, I am learning to add balance to my daily life with meditation, gentler exercise (I only knew, for too long, how to exercise at a fast pace—it was all about cardio, the clock, the race), volunteering as a family and child advocate, prayer and light conversation, to name a few. I do rest, too, and when I can't sleep at night I stay comfortably in bed. I know what the most important use of my time is throughout the day. Whether I'm completing a task, in a meeting, at a fitness class, or sharing time with my family and friends, I'm doing just that at the moment. Feeling, hearing and seeing all that is in that space—all these activities build our physical, emotional and spiritual core strength.

It's been four years since I was diagnosed. Yes, sometimes it's still really hard. Sometimes I struggle with fatigue, neuropathy and chemo brain. But I live, breathe, love and laugh—as trite as that may seem. I fear less than Sally BC. Nevertheless, my journey becomes more surreal as time passes and there are moments when I can't believe that I actually had cancer. It's really all about remaining positive and boldly saying: "I am strong!"; "I can beat this," and "I will be cancer free." I hope you strive to lift yourself to a place and time from which you can look back and know that you did everything in your power to be happy, to be healthy, and to survive.

Remember, being strong does not mean we need to endure pain and be sick because that's just the way chemo goes. Chemo is a very individual thing. Please do not allow or prepare yourself to be lying on the bathroom floor surviving a vomit episode. Medicine has progressed; the treatment process has become more manageable. Today, as a volunteer, I see those patients that do experience nasty symptoms, yet witness nurses investing all they have in responding to and comforting their patients. Be strong means asking for help when you need it. Be strong means taking the anti-nausea medicines. The less we try to control or resist the symptom, the quicker we'll feel calmer and as best we can at any given moment. Be strong touches on all the previous coaching points. It means to push past fear and judgment, and to hold yourself accountable for your care and healing.

Marla ~ Faith

ભ છ

Conclusion

Cancer is a tough fight. One message I want to share is that in every conversation I've had with doctors and survivors, early detection is the common thread. Early detection is your best weapon.

The odds of beating any cancer improves when we catch it early.

Regular screening is vital to early detection. The smaller the tumor, the easier it is to kill. Ask your doctor about Ultrasound testing, as well, and be certain to understand the process in testing and their results. Every step you take, every test you have, should not be done alone. The reality and anxiety of the moment is overwhelming. Seeking the love, guidance and support of our family members and friends is not an elective.

I hope that in my story you will see that beating cancer is a winnable fight. It takes a concentrated effort to adjust to the new normal that is your life from the time of diagnosis until your doctors say that you are cancer free. Everything is touched, everything is moved. My hope for you is that you find your healing path and that the steps I took and the coaching I am sharing will guide you, and make your steps a bit easier. Knowing what's ahead, what to expect, makes the hills a little lower, the twists and turns less surprising.

Please take time for yourself to get past the shock and fear that a cancer diagnosis instills on us all. Fear is cancer's ally in this fight. If you can conquer it first, your victory is within reach. To achieve that victory, you must focus on healing; healing physically, mentally, emotionally and spiritually. Cancer will challenge you, test your strength, on every element of your being. If you can focus on healing by whatever means necessary, and spend time each day doing the things you can to contribute to your healing, making all your treatments, spending time exercising, time in prayer and meditation, understanding what your body is communicating, then you can address the challenge.

Finally, know that by focusing on healing, you will find that it doesn't just attack the cancer, it affects multiple aspects of your life. Focusing on healing can improve other elements of your life, your relationships, your physical fitness, your diet, and the list goes on. I mentioned before, if I am grateful to cancer for anything, it's that I know I am a better person today than I was before I was diagnosed. It's not that I wasn't a caring, decent person then, but I am more engaged today in my physical, mental, emotional and spiritual health than I was then. I live my life purposefully, with a greater sense of gratitude and appreciation. It is my wish that you too, come back stronger from cancer, that you become a better version of you.

Donna ~ Gratitude

ଓଃୡ

About the Author

Sally Nisberg was diagnosed with triple-negative, Stage 2 ductile breast cancer in 2011. Three-years post treatment, she is cancer free and working as a life coach and patient advocate for cancer patients.

She walks and talks cancer everyday, with friends, family and strangers newly diagnosed as patients, and sometimes as victims of this dreadful disease. She works as their advocate to help them through the paralyzing fear that often accompanies those words: "You have cancer" to regain the ability to make positive choices about their care and healing, to begin their journey on a healing path.

This book is Sally's story and her coaching advise to cancer patients, their families and caregivers. It hopes to help more cancer patients and their caregivers understand that though their journey will be unique, some experiences are common and will connect them to other cancer survivors.

Sally is an entrepreneur and life coach. Her business, The Wellness Institute Network (WIN), helps clients gain perspective and balance in their lives, to capture the positive energy they need to thrive. You can check out her blog, *Thoughts on Things*, at thoughtsonthingsblog.com

Sally is an active patient advocate and board member of several community groups:

- KidSanctuary Campus ~ Executive VP, Board of Directors
- PBSO ~ Domestic Violence Advisor
- PBC State Attorney's Office ~ Domestic Violence Advocate
- South Florida Cancer Specialists ~ Patient Advocate

Sally invites you to connect with her and to join the conversation on Facebook, at Thoughtsonthingsblog.com, and at her WIN website wellnessinstitutenetwork.com.

Cらεつ